Day-by-Day Menstrual Cycle Guided Journal

Create a Custom Path to Making Every Day of Your Cycle Better

Volume _____

Gabrielle Lichterman
author of *28 Days: What Your Cycle Reveals About Your Moods, Health and Potential*

PRESS

Published by Hormonology Press
St. Petersburg, Florida, USA

ISBN-13: 978-1-7345983-1-5

Hormonology® Day-by-Day Menstrual Cycle Guided Journal is intended as a reference volume only, not as a medical manual. In light of the complex, individual, and specific nature of health problems, this book is not intended to replace professional medical advice. The ideas, procedures, and suggestions in this book are intended to supplement, not replace, the advice of a trained medical professional. Consult with your physician before adopting the suggestions in this book, as well as about any condition that may require diagnosis or medical attention. The author and publisher disclaim any liability arising directly or indirectly from the use of this book.

This publication is designed to provide accurate and authoritative information with regard to the subject matter covered. It is sold with the understanding that the publisher is not engaged in rendering legal, accounting, or other professional advice. If legal advice or other expert assistance is required, the services of a competent professional should be sought.

—From a *Declaration of Principles* jointly adopted by a Committee of the American Bar Association and a Committee of Publishers and Associations

Hormonology® Day-by-Day Menstrual Cycle Guided Journal is not intended in any way to help you avoid pregnancy or become pregnant. Consult with your healthcare provider before starting any new health, diet, exercise, supplement or herb regimen.

For more information about this book and its author, visit MyHormonology.com.

This book belongs to

_____

CONTENTS

Favorite tips in this book:

_____ .... _____
_____ .... _____
_____ .... _____
_____ .... _____
_____ .... _____
_____ .... _____
_____ .... _____
_____ .... _____
_____ .... _____
_____ .... _____
_____ .... _____
_____ .... _____
_____ .... _____
_____ .... _____
_____ .... _____
_____ .... _____
_____ .... _____

Introduction
Creating a custom path to health and happiness

Thirty-five. That's the average number of years you'll have menstrual cycles in your lifetime. Starting from your tween years and continuing through graduation from secondary school, your first car, your first job, trade school, college, graduate school, marriage, your first house, military service, volunteer missions, motherhood, aunthood, work promotions, business launches, hard-fought competitions, dream vacations, mid-life career changes, planning for retirement and possibly even after becoming a grandmother or great-aunt.

Throughout all of these life events, you'll have a menstrual cycle. This typically means you'll be getting a period every month or so (if you have a uterus and aren't taking continuous hormone birth control).

It also means your hormones will be impacting you from the first day of your period through the day before your next period—and these hormonal influences will affect virtually every aspect of your life: your mood, energy, optimism, confidence, self-esteem, desire to socialize, memory, concentration, romantic attractions, libido, pain sensitivity, how you spend money, patience, resilience, willpower, health issues and much more.

Knowing what you can expect from your period and hormones helps you harness these effects: You'll know when you can capitalize on cycle-related benefits, such as when your mood and energy peak. And, you'll be able to prepare to overcome cycle-related challenges, for example, if you get intense menstrual cramps or when you're experiencing fatigue.

Using this *Hormonology® Day-by-Day Menstrual Cycle Guided Journal*—whether you have a natural cycle (no hormone birth control) or you take hormone birth control—is a vital way to observe, learn and understand how your period and hormones impact you. Then, you can predict and plan for these changes in future cycles.

Even better, you'll be creating a custom path to making every day of your cycle better—with information stemming from your own experience and wisdom. That's because after answering the self-guided questions for each day in your current cycle, you'll have a personalized guide you can turn to in future cycles that reminds you of what makes you happiest and healthiest on each specific cycle day.

Plus, there are lots more benefits. You'll be able to:

- Use it as a tool to sync up activities with the ups and downs of your cycle, such as scheduling big projects on cycle days when your energy is peaking or fun dates with friends on days when you know you'll enjoy socializing
- Pinpoint self-care treatments that reduce stress, improve sleep or make you happier or healthier other ways
- Determine which treatments for cycle-impacted conditions are working and which aren't
- Become familiar with the intensity and frequency of hormonal effects—and what changes them, such as following healthy habits or experiencing stress
- Get in tune with your body's own rhythms

If you want more details about hormonal effects in healthy, natural cycles (meaning no hormone birth control), you can find it in my book, **28 Days: What Your Cycle Reveals About Your Moods, Health and Potential** (available at Amazon). However, you do *not* need **28 Days** to use your **Hormonology® Day-by-Day Menstrual Cycle Guided Journal**. And, you can use this book whether your hormones are natural or you use hormone birth control. This means you can create your custom path to a happier cycle in these pages starting today.

How to Use This Journal

The *Hormonology® Day-by-Day Menstrual Cycle Guided Journal* gives you nine daily guided self-discovery questions that help you to create a custom path to making every day of your cycle better. These questions encourage you to observe the physical, emotional, health and other changes you experience from the first day of your period through the day before your next period. And, they prompt you to write down how to make the most of cycle-related benefits and come up with ways to deal with cycle-related challenges using methods that work best for you. To get started:

1. Decide which cycle day to start journaling

Each chapter of this guided journal corresponds to a single day in your menstrual cycle. At the top of each chapter, you'll be prompted to write the current Day and Week you're on in your cycle. (Not sure where you are in your cycle? To find out, read the following "Menstrual Cycle Know-How" chapter.)

You can wait for your Day 1 (first day of your period) to arrive to start journaling, which you may find simpler. However, you can start journaling today if you know where you are in your cycle.

The Table of Contents contains blank spaces where you'll fill in the Day and Week of each chapter. This makes it easy for you to find each cycle day when you refer back to it in the future.

Note: This book is set up to accommodate cycles lasting up to 50 days. So, you will not need to use the remaining chapters if your cycle is shorter, for example, if it lasts 25 days, 28 days or 32 days. You can leave the remaining pages blank or use them for your own additional notes or needs.

2. Answer the guided self-discovery questions

Write your answers to the nine guided self-discovery questions each day for one full menstrual cycle. Then, return to these pages during each subsequent cycle to be reminded of what makes you happiest on specific cycle days, what is best to avoid on specific cycle days, which health treatments to use, how to prepare for future cycle days and more.

3. Read the bonus tips and advice

Between each chapter, you'll find study-backed tips that help you deal with cycle-related challenges (such as sleep problems and fatigue), cycle-syncing recommendations that show you how to schedule your life using the hormonal rhythms of your cycle and bonus self-discovery questions that give you the opportunity to find more ways to make your cycle even better.

     To make it easier to find tips you've found helpful in the future, list your favorites in the Table of Contents "Favorite tips in this book" section. There are blank spaces for the tip description and its page number.

4. Update your answers in new volumes

Your answers to the self-guided discovery questions will likely shift over time due to changes in health, interests, lifestyle, etc. You can change the answers in this book (by using a pen with erasable ink or pencil) or start another volume of the **Hormonology® Day-by-Day Menstrual Cycle Guided Journal** to create an all-new custom path to healthier, happier cycle days. There is a space on the cover, spine and title page of this book for you to fill in to number your volumes to keep them organized.

Menstrual Cycle Know-How

Where are you in your cycle?

To answer your guided journal questions, you'll need some basics about your cycle. For starters, here's how to know where you are in your cycle:

When your cycle starts

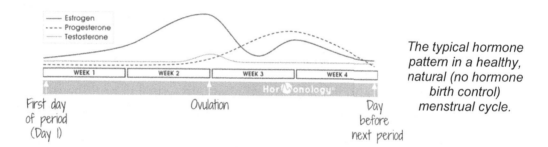

The typical hormone pattern in a healthy, natural (no hormone birth control) menstrual cycle.

Day 1 is the first day of your period. Your period can be light or heavy, but the first day you see red is your Day 1. That's because it means your body's level of estrogen has dropped low enough to signal menstruation. In a natural cycle (no hormone birth control), it also means that estrogen will begin rising again that day, in fact, just a few hours after your period begins.

The day after Day 1 is Day 2 of your cycle. The day after that is Day 3 of your cycle, and so on.

Your entire menstrual cycle lasts from the first day of your period (Day 1) through the day before your next period. The day you get your next period is Day 1 of a new menstrual cycle. Then you start counting all over again.

First half of your cycle

For women with natural cycles and who ovulate, Day 1 through ovulation is the first half of your cycle. This is the "follicular" phase, which gets its name from the follicle that matures in your ovary during this time.

The first half of a natural cycle can vary in length. In fact, the length of this phase typically determines how long your *entire* cycle will be. This means if you have a cycle that's shorter than 28 days, it's because the follicular phase of your cycle was shorter than 14 days. If you have a cycle that's longer than 28 days, it's because this phase of your cycle was longer than 14 days.

Second half of your cycle

The day after ovulation marks the second half of your cycle—the "luteal" phase. It gets this name from a substance in the ovary that's left behind after ovulation called the *corpus luteum* (Latin for "yellow body"), which produces the hormone progesterone.

Your luteal phase is typically a stable number of days. That's because once ovulation occurs, a clock inside your body begins to tick down either to your period or pregnancy. If you didn't get pregnant, then you go on to get your period. For most women, this phase is 14 days long. However, the luteal phase can be slightly shorter or longer, but it's usually still a stable set number of days. Tracking your cycle (for example, with my **Hormonology® Menstrual Cycle Tracker Journal**) can help you pinpoint your luteal phase length.

What this means for you

Once you pinpoint the day you ovulate, you'll count down 14 days (or the number of days in your luteal phase if it's different). The day after that is when you'll get your next period.

Important: There are factors that can alter the length your cycle, such as stress, some medications and certain health conditions. So, the above information is only a general guideline. Tracking your cycle can help you uncover which factors may impact your cycle length.

The difference between "Days" and "Weeks" in a cycle

For the purposes of Hormonology, I use both "Days" and "Weeks" to refer to where you are in a healthy, natural menstrual cycle.

The "Day" you're on refers to how many days it's been since the first day of your period. Day 1 is the day you get your period. Day 2 is the day after that. Day 3 is the day after that. And, so on. The "Week" you're on refers to the *hormonal phase* you're in. Even though I use the word "Week", these phases don't last the traditional seven days. The four Weeks break down like this:

- **Week 1:** The first seven days of your cycle—Day 1 (start of your period) to Day 7. Estrogen begins at its lowest point and slowly rises.
- **Week 2:** Day 8 through ovulation (which is typically Day 14 in a 28-day cycle). Estrogen rises until it peaks. Testosterone rises slightly at the end of Week 2 during ovulation. For Hormonology, Week 2 is the only phase that varies in length.

- **Week 3:** This phase spans the eight days following ovulation (which is Day 15 through Day 22 in a 28-day cycle). Estrogen and testosterone drop during the first three days and estrogen rises again for the rest of this cycle week. Progesterone rises steadily throughout your Week 3.
- **Week 4:** This phase spans the final six days of your cycle (which is Day 23 to Day 28 in a 28-day cycle). Your Week 4 is commonly known as your premenstrual phase. Estrogen and progesterone drop throughout.

I developed these four "Week" categories for Hormonology as a shortcut to figure out where you are in your cycle and what's going on with you hormonally. Each Week has its own "personality" because of the hormone levels and hormone changes going on within it. This makes it easy to know in an instant what to expect simply by knowing which Week you're in. For example, if you're in your Week 1, you'll know that your energy starts off low, but it's increasing day by day. If you're in your Week 2, you'll know that your energy is peaking. If you're in your Week 3, you'll know that your energy is hitting bottom. If you're in your Week 4, you'll know that your energy is getting slightly better than it was in your Week 3, but it's still low compared to Week 2.

You can learn more about how your natural hormones impact your mood, health and behavior every day of your cycle in my book, ***28 Days: What Your Cycle Reveals About Your Moods, Health and Potential*** and at MyHormonology.com.

How to determine when you ovulate

To figure out when you ovulate, there are certain physical symptoms you can look for, which include feeling pain in either ovary (called "mittelschmerz", which is German for "middle pain") and seeing slippery vaginal fluid that resembles raw egg white. However, there are ovulation detection tools (available at drugstores and online) that are more reliable. These include:

- **Basal thermometer:** It detects a subtle increase in your basal (lowest) body temperature that occurs at ovulation due to rising progesterone. To use: Take your temperature every day once you wake up, but before you get out of bed. An increase in temperature of one-half to one degree in the middle of your cycle is a sign that you're ovulating.
- **Ovulation test strips:** These measure the level of luteinizing hormone (LH) that surges one to one-and-a-half days before ovulation. To use: Pass the strip through your urine and if it shows the level of your LH is peaking, you'll be ovulating within 24 to 36 hours.
- **Ovulation microscope:** This lipstick-sized microscope measures the level of salt in your saliva, which peaks at ovulation. To use: Dab saliva on the lens, let dry, then look through the microscope. If you see dots, you're not near ovulation. Dots and lines mean you're nearing ovulation. A fern pattern indicates you're very close to or are ovulating.

Important: Please do not use the information about ovulation or menstrual cycles in this book as a sole form of pregnancy prevention. If you do not use birth control (such as condoms), you can get pregnant on the days leading up to, the day of and the day after ovulation. That's because sperm can survive within your body for up to five days and your egg can survive up to 48 hours. Plus, your ovulation date could have changed due to a number of factors, such as stress, certain medications or illness.

If you're interested in using the natural family planning method—which relies on your body's cues to determine your fertile days—please seek training from a qualified natural family planning instructor.

What if you're taking hormone birth control?

If you take hormone birth control in the form of a pill, patch, ring, shot, implant or IUD, your hormones follow a different pattern than when your hormones are natural (no hormone birth control). There is a wide variation in what those hormone patterns are depending on the type of birth control, but generally speaking, you'll have a "flatter" cycle—meaning, you won't experience the high peaks of Week 2 when estrogen normally spikes. And, you may have a less intense and/or shorter premenstrual phase, which are the days when estrogen and progesterone fall in a natural cycle.

But, no matter which hormone birth control you use, this journal can be a valuable tool that helps you understand how these supplemental hormones impact you day to day, and how to make the most out of each cycle day.

What if you have ovaries, but do not have a uterus?

If your ovaries are fully functioning and you ovulate, but you don't have a uterus, your hormones likely follow an up-and-down pattern similar to someone who does have a uterus. This means you can track hormonal effects and determine where you are in your cycle even without a monthly period. To do so, you'll be using your ovulation date as a guidepost. You can pinpoint ovulation by using the ovulation detection tools I listed. Once you get the sign that you're ovulating, then the next day you'll be entering your luteal phase, which is typically 14 days long. The day following that phase would be your Day 1, indicating a new menstrual cycle.

What if you have an irregular cycle?

If your cycle varies in length (for example, it's 27 days, then 29, then 26), you can still use this menstrual cycle guided journal. To do so, fill out your journal for one full cycle, then rely on ovulation to determine which Day and Week you're on in subsequent cycles. This will keep you on track when you refer back to your journal pages—even if your cycles don't line up exactly. That's because you'll know if you're still in your follicular phase (the first half of your cycle), so you'd re-read those pages until ovulation occurs. And you'll know when you're in your luteal phase (the second half), so you can start reading chapters in your Week 3.

Horonology®
Day-by-Day Menstrual Cycle Guided Journal

How to use:

1. Write down the Day and Week you're on in your menstrual cycle. (To figure out where you are in your cycle, read the "Menstrual Cycle Know-How" chapter.)

2. Answer the nine self-discovery questions about each day of your cycle for one full cycle. (This book accommodates cycles lasting up to 50 days.)

3. Return to these pages during each subsequent cycle to be reminded of what makes you happiest on specific cycle days, what is best to avoid on these cycle days, what treatments worked for certain conditions and more.

4. Add to or update your answers as you learn more about yourself and your cycle.

Tip: Use an erasable pen or pencil to make it easier to correct or change your answers.

Our menstrual cycles mimic
the cycles of nature.

Each month, our hormones wax and wane
like the phases of the moon.

Each week, our cycle is like a new season:
spring, summer, autumn, winter.

We get to experience the wonder of nature
first-hand within ourselves.

-Gabrielle Lichterman

Cycle Day: _____
Cycle Week: _____

What do I notice about myself on this day in my cycle?

_____
_____
_____
_____
_____
_____

What can I appreciate about this day in my cycle?

_____
_____
_____
_____
_____

How can I make this cycle day better?

_____
_____
_____
_____
_____

What is wise
to avoid on
this cycle
day?

_____
_____
_____
_____
_____

_____
_____
_____
_____
_____
_____

What is an
activity that
syncs up
well with
this phase of
my cycle?

What kind of
self-care
would make
me happier
on this
cycle day?

_____
_____
_____
_____
_____
_____

_____

_____

_____

_____

_____

_____

What treatments work for health issues I tend to get today?

What can I do today to make tomorrow better?

_____

_____

_____

_____

_____

_____

_____

_____

_____

_____

_____

What can I do today to make the next week of my cycle better?

Cycle Hack:

Get painful menstrual cramps?
They're the result of hormone-like
chemicals—prostaglandins—that are
triggering spasms in the uterus to push
out menstrual fluid.

One easy remedy: Apply heat to your
pelvic area, for instance, with a warm
washcloth, water bottle, heating pad or
adhesive heat patch (available at
drugstores). Heat blocks pain signals
and relaxes spasming uterine muscles,
lessening discomfort.

SOURCE:
Junyoung Jo, Sun Haeng Lee, "Heat therapy for primary dysmenorrhea: A systematic review and meta-analysis of its effects on pain relief and quality of life," Scientific Reports, 8 (2018): published online November 2, 2018

Cycle Day: _____
Cycle Week: _____

What do I notice about myself on this day in my cycle?

_____
_____
_____
_____
_____
_____

What can I appreciate about this day in my cycle?

_____
_____
_____
_____
_____

How can I make this cycle day better?

_____
_____
_____
_____
_____

What is wise to avoid on this cycle day?

What is an activity that syncs up well with this phase of my cycle?

What kind of self-care would make me happier on this cycle day?

What treatments work for health issues I tend to get today?

_____
_____
_____
_____
_____
_____

What can I do today to make tomorrow better?

_____
_____
_____
_____
_____
_____

What can I do today to make the next week of my cycle better?

_____
_____
_____
_____
_____
_____

?

What are three things you wish you'd
known about your period or hormones when
you started your menstrual cycle
that you're grateful to know now?

Cycle Day: _____
Cycle Week: _____

What do I notice about myself on this day in my cycle?

_____
_____
_____
_____
_____
_____

What can I appreciate about this day in my cycle?

How can I make this cycle day better?

_____
_____
_____
_____
_____
_____

What is wise to avoid on this cycle day?

What is an activity that syncs up well with this phase of my cycle?

What kind of self-care would make me happier on this cycle day?

What treatments work for health issues I tend to get today?

_____
_____
_____
_____
_____
_____

What can I do today to make tomorrow better?

_____
_____
_____
_____
_____
_____

What can I do today to make the next week of my cycle better?

_____
_____
_____
_____
_____
_____

Cycle-Syncing Tip

During your Week 1 (your period week), consider adopting a new healthy habit. A few days after your period starts is an ideal time to launch or relaunch a good-for-you goal, such as starting an exercise routine or quitting smoking. That's because as estrogen rises throughout your Week 1 and Week 2, it gives you more optimism and willpower, making it easier to stick to your new health-boosting routine.

Cycle Day: _____
Cycle Week: _____

What do I notice about myself on this day in my cycle?

_____
_____
_____
_____
_____
_____

_____
_____
_____
_____
_____

What can I appreciate about this day in my cycle?

How can I make this cycle day better?

_____
_____
_____
_____
_____

What is wise to avoid on this cycle day?

_____

_____

_____

_____

_____

_____

_____

_____

_____

_____

_____

What is an activity that syncs up well with this phase of my cycle?

What kind of self-care would make me happier on this cycle day?

_____

_____

_____

_____

_____

_____

What treatments work for health issues I tend to get today?

_____

_____

_____

_____

_____

_____

What can I do today to make tomorrow better?

_____

_____

_____

_____

_____

_____

What can I do today to make the next week of my cycle better?

_____

_____

_____

_____

_____

Cycle Hack:

If you get a migraine at the tail-end of your period or right after your period is over, this is called an "end-menstrual migraine"—and the main culprit is low iron. That's because your iron level drops as you bleed during menstruation, which then disrupts levels of brain chemicals (such as serotonin) that can trigger these painful head-bangers.

This means you may be able to prevent these types of migraines by simply taking a daily iron supplement (15 mg. for ages 14 to 18; 18 mg. for ages 19-50) or eating more iron-rich foods every day avoid this monthly iron dip.

Sources:
Anne H. Calhoun, Nicole Gill, "Presenting a New, Non Hormonally Mediated Cyclic Headache in Women: End Menstrual Migraine," Headache, 57 (2017): 17-20
ods.od.nih.gov/factsheets/Iron-HealthProfessional

Cycle Day: _____
Cycle Week: _____

What do I notice about myself on this day in my cycle?

_____
_____
_____
_____
_____

_____
_____
_____
_____
_____

What can I appreciate about this day in my cycle?

How can I make this cycle day better?

_____
_____
_____
_____
_____

What is wise to avoid on this cycle day?

What is an activity that syncs up well with this phase of my cycle?

What kind of self-care would make me happier on this cycle day?

_____

_____

_____

_____

_____

_____

What treatments work for health issues I tend to get today?

What can I do today to make tomorrow better?

_____

_____

_____

_____

_____

_____

What can I do today to make the next week of my cycle better?

_____

_____

_____

_____

_____

_____

You are doing your healthcare providers a favor by tracking your menstrual cycle. Whether you're visiting for check-ups or you're working on issues for your physical or mental health, sharing your menstrual changes or hormonal effects with your healthcare team can help pinpoint problems, indicate when issues are improving and reveal when you're in balance.

-Gabrielle Lichterman

Cycle Day: _____
Cycle Week: _____

What do I
notice about
myself on
this day in
my cycle?

_____
_____
_____
_____
_____

_____
_____
_____
_____
_____

What can I
appreciate
about this
day in my
cycle?

How can I
make this
cycle day
better?

_____
_____
_____
_____
_____

What is wise to avoid on this cycle day?

_____
_____
_____
_____
_____

_____
_____
_____
_____
_____
_____

What is an activity that syncs up well with this phase of my cycle?

What kind of self-care would make me happier on this cycle day?

_____
_____
_____
_____
_____
_____

What treatments work for health issues I tend to get today?

_____
_____
_____
_____
_____
_____

What can I do today to make tomorrow better?

_____
_____
_____
_____
_____
_____

What can I do today to make the next week of my cycle better?

_____
_____
_____
_____
_____
_____

Cycle Hack:

Do you find that after your period, you're tired, cranky, sad or foggy or have difficulty sleeping? It could be due to low iron.

On the cycle days after your period, rising estrogen is on track to improve your energy, mood and sleep. However, if you're feeling more wiped out, your mood is going south and sleep is restless as the days go on, these are signs that your iron level could have dipped, which is a common issue since you shed iron as you bleed during menstruation.

If low iron is your problem, consider increasing your intake of this mineral via food or supplements all cycle long. It's recommended that women between the ages of 14 and 18 aim for 15 mg. and women between 19 and 50 aim for 18 mg. daily.

Cycle Day: _____
Cycle Week: _____

What do I
notice about
myself on
this day in
my cycle?

_____
_____
_____
_____
_____

_____
_____
_____
_____
_____

What can I
appreciate
about this
day in my
cycle?

How can I
make this
cycle day
better?

_____
_____
_____
_____
_____

What is wise to avoid on this cycle day?

_____

_____

_____

_____

_____

What is an activity that syncs up well with this phase of my cycle?

_____

_____

_____

_____

_____

What kind of self-care would make me happier on this cycle day?

_____

_____

_____

_____

_____

What treatments work for health issues I tend to get today?

_____

_____

_____

_____

_____

_____

What can I do today to make tomorrow better?

_____

_____

_____

_____

_____

_____

What can I do today to make the next week of my cycle better?

_____

_____

_____

_____

_____

_____

?

During Week 2 of your cycle (the week leading up to and including ovulation), your boldness, desire for excitement, confidence and courage all peak thanks to high-and-rising estrogen. This makes it an ideal time to try something new. What are three bold things you want to try?

Cycle Day: _____
Cycle Week: _____

What do I notice about myself on this day in my cycle?

_____
_____
_____
_____
_____
_____

_____
_____
_____
_____
_____
_____

What can I appreciate about this day in my cycle?

How can I make this cycle day better?

_____
_____
_____
_____
_____

What is wise to avoid on this cycle day?

What is an activity that syncs up well with this phase of my cycle?

What kind of self-care would make me happier on this cycle day?

_____

_____

_____

_____

_____

_____

What treatments work for health issues I tend to get today?

What can I do today to make tomorrow better?

_____

_____

_____

_____

_____

_____

_____

_____

_____

_____

What can I do today to make the next week of my cycle better?

Cycle Hack:

Your risk of a vaginal yeast infection rises in your Week 2 (the week leading up to and including ovulation) due to high estrogen, which, unfortunately, helps foster the growth of the infection-causing fungus candida albicans. Your risk also rises in your premenstrual Week 4 due to pH changes in your vaginal tract as estrogen drops.

To reduce your risk: Avoid foods and beverages that feed the fungus. These include alcohol and "simple" carbohydrates (such as sugar and white bread). And consider taking a daily probiotic with the "good" bacteria Lactobacillus acidophilus.

SOURCES:
Georgina Cheng, Kathleen M. Yeater, Lois L. Hoyer, "Cellular and Molecular Biology of Candida albicans Estrogen Response," Eukaryotic Cell, 5 (2006): 180-191
Paul L. Fidel, Jr., Jessica Cutright, Chad Steele, "Effects of Reproductive Hormones on Experimental Vaginal Candidiasis," Infection and Immunity, 68 (2000): 651-657
Eileen Hilton, et al., "Ingestion of Yogurt Containing Lactobacillus acidophilus as Prophylaxis for Candidal Vaginitis," Annals of Internal Medicine, 116 (1992): 353-357

Cycle Day: _____
Cycle Week: _____

What do I notice about myself on this day in my cycle?

_____
_____
_____
_____
_____
_____

_____
_____
_____
_____
_____
_____

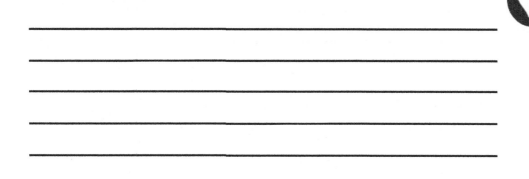

What can I appreciate about this day in my cycle?

How can I make this cycle day better?

_____
_____
_____
_____
_____

What is wise to avoid on this cycle day?

What is an activity that syncs up well with this phase of my cycle?

What kind of self-care would make me happier on this cycle day?

What treatments work for health issues I tend to get today?

_____

_____

_____

_____

_____

_____

What can I do today to make tomorrow better?

_____

_____

_____

_____

_____

_____

What can I do today to make the next week of my cycle better?

_____

_____

_____

_____

_____

_____

Cycle-Syncing Tip

During your Week 2 (the week leading up to and including ovulation), consider learning something new. High-and-rising estrogen is energizing your brain, piquing your curiosity and sharpening your memory, making this an ideal time to pick up a new skill. Take a class, watch an instructional video or ask someone to teach you what they know.

Cycle Day: _____
Cycle Week: _____

What do I notice about myself on this day in my cycle?

_____
_____
_____
_____
_____
_____

What can I appreciate about this day in my cycle?

_____
_____
_____
_____
_____

How can I make this cycle day better?

_____
_____
_____
_____
_____

What is wise to avoid on this cycle day?

What is an activity that syncs up well with this phase of my cycle?

What kind of self-care would make me happier on this cycle day?

What treatments work for health issues I tend to get today?

_____
_____
_____
_____
_____
_____

What can I do today to make tomorrow better?

_____
_____
_____
_____
_____
_____

What can I do today to make the next week of my cycle better?

_____
_____
_____
_____
_____

Cycle Hack:

During your Week 2 (the week leading up to and including ovulation), you could have trouble concentrating. That's because of high estrogen, which ramps up mental energy, making you more easily distracted.

One way to improve focus: Drink green tea. Research shows that the amino acid l-theanine it contains helps calm an overactive brain, while its small amount of caffeine (about 25 mg. per eight-ounce cup) keeps you alert—a combination that can improve attention.

Source:
Suzanne J. Einöther, Vanessa E. Martens, "Acute effects of tea consumption on attention and mood," The American Journal of Clinical Nutrition, 98 (2013): 1700S-1708S

Cycle Day: _____
Cycle Week: _____

What do I notice about myself on this day in my cycle?

_____
_____
_____
_____
_____
_____

_____
_____
_____
_____
_____

What can I appreciate about this day in my cycle?

How can I make this cycle day better?

_____
_____
_____
_____
_____

What is wise to avoid on this cycle day?

What is an activity that syncs up well with this phase of my cycle?

What kind of self-care would make me happier on this cycle day?

What treatments work for health issues I tend to get today?

_____
_____
_____
_____
_____
_____

What can I do today to make tomorrow better?

_____
_____
_____
_____
_____
_____

What can I do today to make the next week of my cycle better?

_____
_____
_____
_____
_____
_____

Cycle Hack:

Have trouble sleeping on certain days in your cycle, for example, during your Week 2 (the week leading up to and including ovulation) due to anxiety if you're sensitive to spiking estrogen? Or during your premenstrual Week 4 due to plunging estrogen disrupting levels of brain chemicals that impact sleep? Try going to bed wearing an anti-nausea acupressure wristband (such as Sea-band, available at drugstores and Amazon). Research shows that this type of wristband presses a certain acupressure point on your wrist ("Shen Men") that helps you relax so you fall asleep faster and get higher-quality sleep.

Sources:
Marco Carotenuto, et al., "Acupressure therapy for insomnia in adolescents: a polysomnographic study," Neuropsychiatric Disease and Treatment, 9 (2013): 157-162
Mei-Jou Lu, et al., "Acupressure improves sleep quality of psychogeriatric inpatients," Nursing Research, 62 (2013): 130-137

Cycle Day: _____
Cycle Week: _____

What do I notice about myself on this day in my cycle?

_____
_____
_____
_____
_____
_____

_____
_____
_____
_____
_____
_____

What can I appreciate about this day in my cycle?

How can I make this cycle day better?

_____
_____
_____
_____
_____
_____

What is wise to avoid on this cycle day?

What is an activity that syncs up well with this phase of my cycle?

What kind of self-care would make me happier on this cycle day?

What treatments work for health issues I tend to get today?

_____
_____
_____
_____
_____
_____

What can I do today to make tomorrow better?

_____
_____
_____
_____
_____
_____

What can I do today to make the next week of my cycle better?

_____
_____
_____
_____
_____
_____

Mittelschmerz alert:

Get a sharp pain on one side of your pelvis at ovulation?

It could be "mittelschmerz" (which aptly rhymes with "middle hurts").

This mid-cycle pain is a common side effect of ovulation that's experienced by at least one in five of those who ovulate.

It can happen every cycle, every so often, or just once in a long while.

To ease the pain, you can apply a heat patch or hot water bottle to your pelvic region until it passes.

Cycle Day: _____
Cycle Week: _____

What do I notice about myself on this day in my cycle?

_____
_____
_____
_____
_____

_____
_____
_____
_____
_____
_____

What can I appreciate about this day in my cycle?

How can I make this cycle day better?

_____
_____
_____
_____
_____
_____

What is wise
to avoid on
this cycle
day?

What is an
activity that
syncs up
well with
this phase of
my cycle?

What kind of
self-care
would make
me happier
on this
cycle day?

_____

_____

_____

_____

_____

_____

What treatments work for health issues I tend to get today?

What can I do today to make tomorrow better?

_____

_____

_____

_____

_____

_____

What can I do today to make the next week of my cycle better?

_____

_____

_____

_____

_____

_____

Until recently, virtually everything we heard about our hormones and menstrual cycles was negative. Generations were told that our cycles make us cranky, sad, tired, crazy.

But, we educated ourselves about our cycles and now we know better. They can be a source of strength, hope, inspiration, confidence, creativity.

We have flipped the script. And now generations will hear about that.

-Gabrielle Lichterman

Cycle Day: _____
Cycle Week: _____

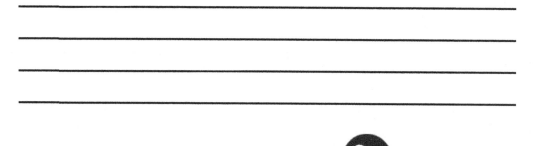

What do I notice about myself on this day in my cycle?

_____
_____
_____
_____
_____
_____

_____
_____
_____
_____
_____
_____

What can I appreciate about this day in my cycle?

How can I make this cycle day better?

_____
_____
_____
_____
_____
_____

What is wise to avoid on this cycle day?

What is an activity that syncs up well with this phase of my cycle?

What kind of self-care would make me happier on this cycle day?

_____

What treatments work for health issues I tend to get today?

_____
_____
_____
_____
_____

What can I do today to make tomorrow better?

_____
_____
_____
_____
_____
_____

_____
_____
_____
_____
_____

What can I do today to make the next week of my cycle better?

?

What is something you wish someone in your life
(such as a family member, healthcare provider,
friend or partner) knew about your cycle that this
person does not know now...and three possible ways
you could comfortably share it?

Cycle Day: _____
Cycle Week: _____

What do I notice about myself on this day in my cycle?

_____
_____
_____
_____
_____

_____
_____
_____
_____
_____

What can I appreciate about this day in my cycle?

How can I make this cycle day better?

_____
_____
_____
_____
_____

What is wise to avoid on this cycle day?

What is an activity that syncs up well with this phase of my cycle?

What kind of self-care would make me happier on this cycle day?

What treatments work for health issues I tend to get today?

_____
_____
_____
_____
_____
_____

What can I do today to make tomorrow better?

_____
_____
_____
_____
_____
_____

What can I do today to make the next week of my cycle better?

_____
_____
_____
_____
_____

Cycle-Syncing Tip

During your Week 3 (the eight days following ovulation), sedating progesterone rises, mellowing you out. If this hormonal shift makes you miss the high energy of your Week 2 (caused by spiking estrogen), give yourself reasons to love your slower-paced Week 3. One way to do this: Find activities you enjoy that match the gentler pace of this cycle phase, such as soaking in a warm bath, reading a book, watching a documentary or taking a leisurely walk.

Cycle Day: _____
Cycle Week: _____

What do I notice about myself on this day in my cycle?

What can I appreciate about this day in my cycle?

How can I make this cycle day better?

What is wise to avoid on this cycle day?

What is an activity that syncs up well with this phase of my cycle?

What kind of self-care would make me happier on this cycle day?

_____

_____

_____

_____

_____

_____

What treatments work for health issues I tend to get today?

What can I do today to make tomorrow better?

_____

_____

_____

_____

_____

_____

_____

_____

_____

_____

_____

_____

What can I do today to make the next week of my cycle better?

Cycle Hack:

It's normal to feel a bit mentally foggy at certain points in your cycle, such as during your Week 3 (the 8 days following ovulation) when sedating progesterone rises. To rev mental alertness, try drinking peppermint tea. Researchers found that one cup temporarily improves long-term memory (needed to recall information you learned awhile ago) and working memory (the kind needed to juggle multiple pieces of information right now). Credit goes to peppermint's menthol and rosmarinic acid, which trigger alertness and increase levels of the memory-sharpening neurotransmitter acetylcholine in the brain.

Source:
Mark Moss, et al. "Acute consumption of Peppermint and Chamomile teas produce contrasting effects on cognition and mood in healthy young adults," Plant Science Today, 3 (2016): 327-336

Cycle Day: _____

Cycle Week: _____

What do I notice about myself on this day in my cycle?

_____
_____
_____
_____
_____
_____

_____
_____
_____
_____
_____

What can I appreciate about this day in my cycle?

How can I make this cycle day better?

_____
_____
_____
_____
_____

What is wise to avoid on this cycle day?

What is an activity that syncs up well with this phase of my cycle?

What kind of self-care would make me happier on this cycle day?

What treatments work for health issues I tend to get today?

_____
_____
_____
_____
_____
_____

What can I do today to make tomorrow better?

_____
_____
_____
_____
_____
_____

What can I do today to make the next week of my cycle better?

_____
_____
_____
_____
_____
_____

?

During the second half of your cycle (your Week 3 and Week 4), you're more prone to beating yourself up when things go wrong. What are three statements you can tell yourself or actions you can take that would help you feel better when mistakes occur?

Cycle Day: _____
Cycle Week: _____

What do I notice about myself on this day in my cycle?

_____
_____
_____
_____
_____

_____
_____
_____
_____
_____

What can I appreciate about this day in my cycle?

How can I make this cycle day better?

_____
_____
_____
_____
_____

What is wise to avoid on this cycle day?

What is an activity that syncs up well with this phase of my cycle?

What kind of self-care would make me happier on this cycle day?

What
treatments
work for
health issues
I tend to get
today?

_____
_____
_____
_____
_____
_____

What can I
do today to
make
tomorrow
better?

_____
_____
_____
_____
_____
_____

What can I
do today to
make the
next week of
my cycle
better?

_____
_____
_____
_____
_____

Cycle Hack:

Experiencing harder stool or constipation in the second half of your cycle is common due to elevated progesterone. One way to get things moving: Snack on dried plums (also known as prunes). Research shows that this old-fashioned constipation remedy works more effectively than psyillium-containing fiber additives at making you regular thanks to their sorbitol, a sugar alcohol that has a mild laxative effect.

SOURCE:
Ashok Attaluri, et al., "Randomised clinical trial: dried plums (prunes) vs. psyllium for constipation," Alimentary Pharmacology & Therapeutics, 33 (2011): 822-828

Cycle Day: _____
Cycle Week: _____

What do I notice about myself on this day in my cycle?

_____
_____
_____
_____
_____
_____

_____
_____
_____
_____
_____

What can I appreciate about this day in my cycle?

How can I make this cycle day better?

_____
_____
_____
_____
_____
_____

What is wise to avoid on this cycle day?

What is an activity that syncs up well with this phase of my cycle?

What kind of self-care would make me happier on this cycle day?

What treatments work for health issues I tend to get today?

_____
_____
_____
_____
_____
_____

What can I do today to make tomorrow better?

_____
_____
_____
_____
_____
_____

What can I do today to make the next week of my cycle better?

_____
_____
_____
_____
_____

Cycle Hack:

Get hit with sudden and intense bouts of irritability, sadness or fatigue during your Week 3 or Week 4 (the second half of your cycle)? You could be hungry! Elevated progesterone on these cycle days makes many women more sensitive to drops in blood sugar between meals, which can spark unexpected changes in mood and energy. The fix? Eat! Nibbling a snack at the first sign of hunger helps keep you on an even keel. And, if your mood or energy has already dropped, eating can bring you back to a happier, more alert state within minutes.

SOURCES:
Safar Zarei, Leili Mosalanejad, Mohamed Amin Ghobadifar, "Blood glucose levels, insulin concentrations, and insulin resistance in healthy women and women with premenstrual syndrome: a comparative study," Clinical and Experimental Reproductive Medicine, 40 (2013): 76-82
Michael P. Diamond, Donald C. Simonson, Ralph A. DeFronzo, "Menstrual cyclicity has a profound effect on glucose homeostasis," Fertility and Sterility, 52 (1989): 204-208

Cycle Day: _____
Cycle Week: _____

What do I notice about myself on this day in my cycle?

_____
_____
_____
_____
_____

_____
_____
_____
_____
_____

What can I appreciate about this day in my cycle?

How can I make this cycle day better?

_____
_____
_____
_____
_____

What is wise to avoid on this cycle day?

What is an activity that syncs up well with this phase of my cycle?

What kind of self-care would make me happier on this cycle day?

_____

_____

_____

_____

_____

_____

What treatments work for health issues I tend to get today?

What can I do today to make tomorrow better?

_____

_____

_____

_____

_____

_____

What can I do today to make the next week of my cycle better?

_____

_____

_____

_____

_____

_____

"

When you're faced with a challenge related to the ups and downs of hormones in your cycle, such as sadness or anxiety, try to remind yourself that it's temporary and will pass.

-Gabrielle Lichterman

Cycle Day: _____
Cycle Week: _____

What do I notice about myself on this day in my cycle?

_____
_____
_____
_____
_____
_____

_____
_____
_____
_____
_____
_____

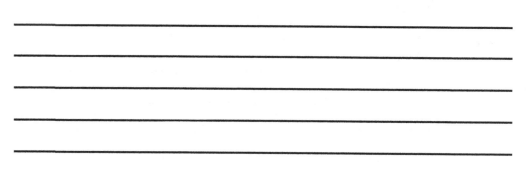

What can I appreciate about this day in my cycle?

How can I make this cycle day better?

_____
_____
_____
_____
_____

What is wise to avoid on this cycle day?

What is an activity that syncs up well with this phase of my cycle?

What kind of self-care would make me happier on this cycle day?

_____

_____

_____

_____

_____

_____

What treatments work for health issues I tend to get today?

What can I do today to make tomorrow better?

_____

_____

_____

_____

_____

_____

_____

_____

_____

_____

_____

What can I do today to make the next week of my cycle better?

Cycle Hack:

Need a caffeine-free energy boost on slower cycle days, such as the start of your period when estrogen is low or right after ovulation when sedating progesterone rises? Get moving! Sounds counterintuitive, but when you're fatigued, climbing stairs, walking or being active another way actually revs energy. In fact, one study on tired women found that stair climbing (at any speed) worked better at increasing pep than downing a caffeinated beverage. Why? Moving increases circulation, which shakes off fogginess.

SOURCE:
Derek D. Randolph, Patrick J. O'Connor, "Stair walking is more energizing than low dose caffeine in sleep deprived young women," Physiology & Behavior, 174 (2017): 128-135

Cycle Day: _____
Cycle Week: _____

What do I notice about myself on this day in my cycle?

_____
_____
_____
_____
_____

What can I appreciate about this day in my cycle?

How can I make this cycle day better?

_____
_____
_____
_____
_____

What is wise to avoid on this cycle day?

What is an activity that syncs up well with this phase of my cycle?

What kind of self-care would make me happier on this cycle day?

What treatments work for health issues I tend to get today?

_____
_____
_____
_____
_____
_____

What can I do today to make tomorrow better?

_____
_____
_____
_____
_____
_____

What can I do today to make the next week of my cycle better?

_____
_____
_____
_____
_____
_____

PMDD alert:

Are your premenstrual symptoms so severe
that they interfere with your everyday life?

For example, do you experience depression,
anxiety, thoughts of self-harm, intense pain,
debilitating fatigue or insomnia?

Do these symptoms begin soon after ovulation?

You could have premenstrual dysphoric
disorder (PMDD), a condition that impacts an
estimated 1 in 10 with menstrual cycles.

If you think you may have PMDD, please talk
with your healthcare providers about it.

And join PMDD education and support groups,
such as the International Association
for Premenstrual Disorders (iapmd.org),
Integrative Institute for PMDD
(integrativepmdd.org) and
Vicious Cycle (viciouscyclepmdd.com).

There is help.

Cycle Day: _____
Cycle Week: _____

What do I notice about myself on this day in my cycle?

_____
_____
_____
_____
_____
_____

_____
_____
_____
_____
_____

What can I appreciate about this day in my cycle?

How can I make this cycle day better?

_____
_____
_____
_____
_____

What is wise to avoid on this cycle day?

What is an activity that syncs up well with this phase of my cycle?

What kind of self-care would make me happier on this cycle day?

_____
_____
_____
_____
_____
_____

What treatments work for health issues I tend to get today?

What can I do today to make tomorrow better?

_____
_____
_____
_____
_____

_____
_____
_____
_____
_____

What can I do today to make the next week of my cycle better?

Cycle Hack:

Get angry a lot during your premenstrual phase? It may not be hormones. You may need to up your zinc or iron. A deficiency in these minerals can lead to more anger and irritability because they're needed to help create mood-regulating serotonin in the brain. You can get zinc and iron from food or supplements.
The recommended daily intake for zinc is 9 mg. for women ages 14 to 18 and 8 mg. for women 19 and older.
For iron, it's 15 mg. for women ages 14 to 18 and 18 mg. for women 19 to 50.

Sources:
Takako Sawada, Katsuhiko Yokoi, "Effect of zinc supplementation on mood states in young women: a pilot study," European Journal of Clinical Nutrition, 64 (2010): 331-333
Takako Sawada, Aki Konomi, Katsuhiko Yokoi, "Iron Deficiency Without Anemia Is Associated with Anger and Fatigue in Young Japanese Women," Biological Trace Element Research, 159 (2014): 22-31
ods.od.nih.gov/factsheets/Zinc-HealthProfessional
ods.od.nih.gov/factsheets/Iron-HealthProfessional

Cycle Day: _____

Cycle Week: _____

What do I notice about myself on this day in my cycle?

_____
_____
_____
_____
_____

_____
_____
_____
_____
_____

What can I appreciate about this day in my cycle?

How can I make this cycle day better?

_____
_____
_____
_____
_____

What is wise to avoid on this cycle day?

What is an activity that syncs up well with this phase of my cycle?

What kind of self-care would make me happier on this cycle day?

What treatments work for health issues I tend to get today?

_____

_____

_____

_____

_____

What can I do today to make tomorrow better?

_____

_____

_____

_____

_____

_____

What can I do today to make the next week of my cycle better?

_____

_____

_____

_____

_____

_____

Cycle-Syncing Tip

During your Week 4 (your premenstrual phase), be sure to create a back-up plan for activities, shopping, socializing, dates, movies, restaurants or anything else you want to do. Plunging estrogen can sap your patience and sour your mood when things don't go as intended (for example, a restaurant loses your reservation or a pal changes her mind about going out).

But, when you have a Plan B in place that you already like, you'll be able to pivot immediately to your second choice, keeping your mood up.

Cycle Day: _____
Cycle Week: _____

What do I notice about myself on this day in my cycle?

_____
_____
_____
_____
_____
_____

_____
_____
_____
_____
_____
_____

What can I appreciate about this day in my cycle?

How can I make this cycle day better?

_____
_____
_____
_____
_____

What is wise to avoid on this cycle day?

What is an activity that syncs up well with this phase of my cycle?

What kind of self-care would make me happier on this cycle day?

_____

_____

_____

_____

_____

_____

What treatments work for health issues I tend to get today?

What can I do today to make tomorrow better?

_____

_____

_____

_____

_____

_____

_____

_____

_____

_____

_____

_____

What can I do today to make the next week of my cycle better?

?

During the second half of your cycle
(your Week 3 and Week 4), you tend to ruminate
longer, mulling over past hurts or current
irritations, due to two drops in estrogen. What
are three things you can say or do to halt these
types of thoughts when you notice them?

Cycle Day: _____
Cycle Week: _____

What do I notice about myself on this day in my cycle?

_____
_____
_____
_____
_____

_____
_____
_____
_____
_____

What can I appreciate about this day in my cycle?

How can I make this cycle day better?

_____
_____
_____
_____
_____

What is wise
to avoid on
this cycle
day?

_____
_____
_____
_____
_____

_____
_____
_____
_____
_____

What is an
activity that
syncs up
well with
this phase of
my cycle?

What kind of
self-care
would make
me happier
on this
cycle day?

_____
_____
_____
_____
_____

_____
_____
_____
_____
_____
_____

What treatments work for health issues I tend to get today?

What can I do today to make tomorrow better?

_____
_____
_____
_____
_____
_____

What can I do today to make the next week of my cycle better?

_____
_____
_____
_____
_____

Cycle Hack:

Want an easy way to improve a premenstrual mood? Try inhaling a lavender, Damask rose or yuzu (a type of citrus fruit) scent. All of these aromas have been shown in studies to usher in calm and bolster mood by creating changes in the brain that manage emotions.

SOURCES:
Tamaki Matsumoto, Hiroyuki Asakura, Tatsuya Hayashi, "Does lavender aromatherapy alleviate premenstrual emotional symptoms?: a randomized crossover trial," BioPsychoSocial Medicine, 7 (2013): published online May 31, 2013
Tapanee Hongratanaworakit, "Relaxing effect of rose oil on humans," Natural Product Communications, 4 (2009): 291-296
Tamaki Matsumoto, Tetsuya Kimura, Tatsuya Hayashi, "Does Japanese Citrus Fruit Yuzu (Citrus junos Sieb. ex Tanaka) Fragrance Have Lavender-Like Therapeutic Effects That Alleviate Premenstrual Emotional Symptoms? A Single-Blind Randomized Crossover Study," Journal of Alternative and Complementary Medicine, 23 (2017): published online June 1, 2017

Cycle Day: _____
Cycle Week: _____

What do I notice about myself on this day in my cycle?

_____
_____
_____
_____
_____

_____
_____
_____
_____
_____

What can I appreciate about this day in my cycle?

How can I make this cycle day better?

_____
_____
_____
_____
_____

What is wise to avoid on this cycle day?

What is an activity that syncs up well with this phase of my cycle?

What kind of self-care would make me happier on this cycle day?

What
treatments
work for
health issues
I tend to get
today?

_____
_____
_____
_____
_____
_____

What can I
do today to
make
tomorrow
better?

_____
_____
_____
_____
_____
_____

What can I
do today to
make the
next week of
my cycle
better?

_____
_____
_____
_____
_____

I'm regularly asked:
"If I change every week of my
monthly cycle—getting more
outgoing or shy, daring or safe, silly
or serious, experimental or
traditional—then which cycle week
is the 'real' me?"

My answer: They're *all* the real you.

Your personality is not a fixed dot.
It's a wide spectrum.

The ups and downs of hormones
help shift you across that spectrum—
the spectrum that makes up *you*.

-Gabrielle Lichterman

Cycle Day: _____
Cycle Week: _____

What do I notice about myself on this day in my cycle?

_____
_____
_____
_____
_____
_____

_____
_____
_____
_____
_____

What can I appreciate about this day in my cycle?

How can I make this cycle day better?

_____
_____
_____
_____
_____
_____

What is wise
to avoid on
this cycle
day?

What is an
activity that
syncs up
well with
this phase of
my cycle?

What kind of
self-care
would make
me happier
on this
cycle day?

_____

What treatments work for health issues I tend to get today?

_____
_____
_____
_____
_____

What can I do today to make tomorrow better?

_____
_____
_____
_____
_____
_____

_____

What can I do today to make the next week of my cycle better?

_____
_____
_____
_____
_____

Cycle Hack:

For a happier, healthier cycle, try yoga! Numerous studies show it boosts a premenstrual mood, eases cycle-related pain, improves sleep and helps regulate menstrual cycle length. Credit goes to its ability to reduce stress by calming overactive systems in your brain and body as well as teaching you positive coping mechanisms (such as slow breathing and mindfulness) that make you more resilient.

SOURCES:
Jennifer Oates, "The Effect of Yoga on Menstrual Disorders: A Systematic Review," The Journal of Alternative and Complementary Medicine, 23, June 1, 2017
Ghafoureh Ghaffarilaleh, et al., "Effects of Yoga on Quality of Sleep of Women With Premenstrual Syndrome," Alternative Therapies in Health and Medicine, 25 (2019): 40-47

Cycle Day: _____
Cycle Week: _____

What do I notice about myself on this day in my cycle?

_____
_____
_____
_____
_____
_____

_____
_____
_____
_____
_____

What can I appreciate about this day in my cycle?

How can I make this cycle day better?

_____
_____
_____
_____
_____

What is wise to avoid on this cycle day?

What is an activity that syncs up well with this phase of my cycle?

What kind of self-care would make me happier on this cycle day?

What treatments work for health issues I tend to get today?

_____

_____

_____

_____

_____

_____

What can I do today to make tomorrow better?

_____

_____

_____

_____

_____

_____

What can I do today to make the next week of my cycle better?

_____

_____

_____

_____

_____

_____

Cycle-Syncing Tip

When waking up to a new day,
try to think of ways you can capitalize on today's
hormonal strengths, for example, going for a run in
your Week 2 (the week leading up to and including
ovulation) when energy peaks due to high-and-rising
estrogen or editing a manuscript in your Week 3 (the
eight days following ovulation) when it's easier to focus
for longer periods of time due to rising progesterone.

It'll help make your day better. And it'll help you
appreciate your hormonal rhythms even more.

Cycle Day: _____
Cycle Week: _____

What do I notice about myself on this day in my cycle?

_____
_____
_____
_____
_____

_____
_____
_____
_____
_____

What can I appreciate about this day in my cycle?

How can I make this cycle day better?

_____
_____
_____
_____
_____

What is wise to avoid on this cycle day?

What is an activity that syncs up well with this phase of my cycle?

What kind of self-care would make me happier on this cycle day?

What treatments work for health issues I tend to get today?

_____

_____

_____

_____

_____

What can I do today to make tomorrow better?

_____

_____

_____

_____

_____

_____

What can I do today to make the next week of my cycle better?

_____

_____

_____

_____

_____

Cycle Hack:

Blue? Cranky? Foggy? Tired? These may sound like hormone issues, but you could simply need a drink of water. Research shows that even mild dehydration can trigger these bothersome symptoms. That's because brain cells require a certain amount of fluid to function at their best. Fortunately, if your symptoms are dehydration-related, simply downing a glass of water or other replenishing beverage can help reverse them in minutes!

SOURCES:
Natalie A. Masento, et al., "Effects of hydration status on cognitive performance and mood," British Journal of Nutrition, 111 (2014): 1841-52
Lawrence E. Armstrong, et al., "Mild Dehydration Affects Mood in Healthy Young Women," The Journal of Nutrition, 2 (2012): 382-388

Cycle Day: _____
Cycle Week: _____

What do I notice about myself on this day in my cycle?

_____
_____
_____
_____
_____

_____
_____
_____
_____
_____

What can I appreciate about this day in my cycle?

How can I make this cycle day better?

_____
_____
_____
_____
_____

What is wise to avoid on this cycle day?

What is an activity that syncs up well with this phase of my cycle?

What kind of self-care would make me happier on this cycle day?

What treatments work for health issues I tend to get today?

_____
_____
_____
_____
_____
_____

What can I do today to make tomorrow better?

_____
_____
_____
_____
_____
_____

What can I do today to make the next week of my cycle better?

_____
_____
_____
_____
_____

Cycle Hack:

Experiencing harder stool or constipation in the second half of your cycle is common due to elevated progesterone. One way to get things moving: Eat rye bread. One study found this tasty food works more effectively than laxatives and probiotics at relieving constipation thanks to a type of fiber it contains that ferments in the intestine and triggers contractions that make stuck contents move. What's more, it does the job without cramping or other uncomfortable side effects.

SOURCE:
Reetta Holma, et al., "Constipation Is Relieved More by Rye Bread Than Wheat Bread or Laxatives without Increased Adverse Gastrointestinal Effects," The Journal of Nutrition, 140 (2010):534-541

Cycle Day: _____
Cycle Week: _____

What do I notice about myself on this day in my cycle?

_____
_____
_____
_____
_____
_____

What can I appreciate about this day in my cycle?

How can I make this cycle day better?

_____
_____
_____
_____
_____

What is wise to avoid on this cycle day?

What is an activity that syncs up well with this phase of my cycle?

What kind of self-care would make me happier on this cycle day?

What treatments work for health issues I tend to get today?

_____

_____

_____

_____

_____

What can I do today to make tomorrow better?

_____

_____

_____

_____

_____

_____

What can I do today to make the next week of my cycle better?

_____

_____

_____

_____

_____

Cycle Hack:

Need a mood and brain reset in your premenstrual phase? Take a nap. In one study, premenstrual women felt cheerier, more relaxed, mentally sharper and more alert after taking a 30-minute afternoon nap than premenstrual women who simply rested for the same amount of time. Why it works: You may be getting lighter, less refreshing sleep during your premenstrual phase due to plunging estrogen—so these extra afternoon zzzs help make up for the sleep deficit, giving you a reboot.

SOURCE:
Lynne J. Lamarche, "Napping during the late luteal phase improves sleepiness, alertness, mood and cognitive performance in women with and without premenstrual symptoms," Sleep and Biological Rhythms, 8 (2010): 151-159

Cycle Day: _____
Cycle Week: _____

What do I notice about myself on this day in my cycle?

_____
_____
_____
_____
_____

_____
_____
_____
_____
_____

What can I appreciate about this day in my cycle?

How can I make this cycle day better?

_____
_____
_____
_____
_____

What is wise to avoid on this cycle day?

_____
_____
_____
_____
_____

What is an activity that syncs up well with this phase of my cycle?

_____
_____
_____
_____
_____

What kind of self-care would make me happier on this cycle day?

_____
_____
_____
_____
_____

What treatments work for health issues I tend to get today?

_____
_____
_____
_____
_____
_____

What can I do today to make tomorrow better?

_____
_____
_____
_____
_____
_____

What can I do today to make the next week of my cycle better?

_____
_____
_____
_____
_____

Try to avoid viewing a
particular day or phase of
your cycle as the
"best" or "worst".

Each is different and brings
with it its own unique
benefits and challenges.

Understanding this helps
you embrace every day of
your cycle.

-Gabrielle Lichterman

Cycle Day: _____
Cycle Week: _____

What do I notice about myself on this day in my cycle?

_____
_____
_____
_____
_____

_____
_____
_____
_____
_____

What can I appreciate about this day in my cycle?

How can I make this cycle day better?

_____
_____
_____
_____
_____

What is wise
to avoid on
this cycle
day?

_____

What is an
activity that
syncs up
well with
this phase of
my cycle?

What kind of
self-care
would make
me happier
on this
cycle day?

_____
_____
_____
_____
_____
_____

What treatments work for health issues I tend to get today?

What can I do today to make tomorrow better?

_____
_____
_____
_____
_____
_____

_____
_____
_____
_____
_____

What can I do today to make the next week of my cycle better?

Cycle Hack:

On cycle days when good sleep is harder to come by, try placing a lavender-scented sachet by your bedside. Researchers found that folks who followed healthy sleep habits while also inhaling lavender throughout the night enjoyed better, deeper sleep than those who followed healthy sleep habits alone.
Why it works? Lavender contains compounds (such as linalool) that trigger relaxation when inhaled.

SOURCE:
Angela Smith Lillehei, et al., "Effect of Inhaled Lavender and Sleep Hygiene on Self-Reported Sleep Issues: A Randomized Controlled Trial," Journal of Alternative and Complementary Medicine, 21 (2015): 430-438

Cycle Day: _____
Cycle Week: _____

What do I notice about myself on this day in my cycle?

_____
_____
_____
_____
_____
_____

_____
_____
_____
_____
_____
_____

What can I appreciate about this day in my cycle?

How can I make this cycle day better?

_____
_____
_____
_____
_____
_____

What is wise to avoid on this cycle day?

_____
_____
_____
_____
_____

_____
_____
_____
_____
_____

What is an activity that syncs up well with this phase of my cycle?

What kind of self-care would make me happier on this cycle day?

_____
_____
_____
_____
_____

_____

What treatments work for health issues I tend to get today?

_____
_____
_____
_____
_____

What can I do today to make tomorrow better?

_____
_____
_____
_____
_____
_____

What can I do today to make the next week of my cycle better?

_____
_____
_____
_____
_____
_____

Learning how
hormones in your
menstrual cycle
impact your brain and
body is just as
important as learning
how nutrition,
exercise, sleep habits
and stress impact
your brain and body.

-Gabrielle Lichterman

Cycle Day: _____
Cycle Week: _____

What do I notice about myself on this day in my cycle?

_____
_____
_____
_____
_____
_____

_____
_____
_____
_____
_____

What can I appreciate about this day in my cycle?

How can I make this cycle day better?

_____
_____
_____
_____
_____

What is wise to avoid on this cycle day?

What is an activity that syncs up well with this phase of my cycle?

What kind of self-care would make me happier on this cycle day?

What treatments work for health issues I tend to get today?

_____
_____
_____
_____
_____
_____

What can I do today to make tomorrow better?

_____
_____
_____
_____
_____
_____

What can I do today to make the next week of my cycle better?

_____
_____
_____
_____
_____

Cycle Hack:

During your Week 3 and Week 4
(the second half of your cycle),
keep hydrating fluids nearby if you're
exercising, playing sports or are active
other ways, especially in hot, humid
environments. You tend to perspire
more on these cycle days due to a
slightly higher core body temperature
caused by elevated progesterone. This
means you could sweat out fluids
more quickly, so you may need to
replenish more frequently.

SOURCE:
Haneul Lee, et al, "Higher Sweating Rate and Skin Blood Flow during the Luteal Phase of the Menstrual Cycle," The Tohoku Journal of Experimental Medicine, 234 (2014): 117-122.

Cycle Day: _____
Cycle Week: _____

What do I notice about myself on this day in my cycle?

_____
_____
_____
_____
_____

_____
_____
_____
_____

What can I appreciate about this day in my cycle?

How can I make this cycle day better?

_____
_____
_____
_____
_____

What is wise to avoid on this cycle day?

What is an activity that syncs up well with this phase of my cycle?

What kind of self-care would make me happier on this cycle day?

What treatments work for health issues I tend to get today?

_____
_____
_____
_____
_____
_____

What can I do today to make tomorrow better?

_____
_____
_____
_____
_____
_____

What can I do today to make the next week of my cycle better?

_____
_____
_____
_____
_____
_____

Cycle Hack:

To clock longer, deeper sleep throughout your cycle, spend more time with folks you enjoy. Research shows that those who regularly talk and visit with supportive friends and family enjoy higher-quality zzzs. Why? Being reminded of the loving support of others boosts mood and decreases stress—two keys to a good night's rest.

Want to find more caring pals to help you get better sleep? Try joining a club that focuses on supporting its members, such as a group for exercisers, knitters, photographers, visual artists or writers.

SOURCE:
Robert G. Kent, et al., "Social Relationships and Sleep Quality," Annals of Behavioral Medicine, 49 (2015): 912-917

Cycle Day: _____
Cycle Week: _____

What do I notice about myself on this day in my cycle?

_____
_____
_____
_____
_____

_____
_____
_____
_____
_____

What can I appreciate about this day in my cycle?

How can I make this cycle day better?

_____
_____
_____
_____
_____

What is wise to avoid on this cycle day?

What is an activity that syncs up well with this phase of my cycle?

What kind of self-care would make me happier on this cycle day?

_____

_____

_____

_____

_____

_____

What treatments work for health issues I tend to get today?

What can I do today to make tomorrow better?

_____

_____

_____

_____

_____

_____

_____

_____

_____

_____

_____

_____

What can I do today to make the next week of my cycle better?

Cycle Hack:

Have an unusually long menstrual cycle—longer than 35 days? Have a cycle that varies in length from month to month? Let your gynecologist know to rule out problems. If there aren't any, try taking a daily dose of vitamin D3 (the supplement form of vitamin D).

Researchers suspect vitamin D may play a role in regulating hormones that affect ovarian function. So, if your body's store of this nutrient dips too low, it could throw off your cycle, making it less regular. The recommended daily amount: 600 IU.

SOURCES:
Anne Marie Z.Jukic, et al., "Increasing serum 25-hydroxyvitamin D is associated with reduced odds of long menstrual cycles in a cross-sectional study of African American women," Fertility and Sterility, 1 (2016): 172-179.e2
Anne Marie Z. Jukic, Anne Z. Steiner, Donna D. Baird, "Lower plasma 25-hydroxyvitamin D is associated with irregular menstrual cycles in a cross-sectional study," Reproductive Biology and Endocrinology, 13 (2015): 20
ods.od.nih.gov/factsheets/VitaminD-Consumer

Cycle Day: _____
Cycle Week: _____

What do I notice about myself on this day in my cycle?

_____
_____
_____
_____
_____
_____

_____
_____
_____
_____
_____

What can I appreciate about this day in my cycle?

How can I make this cycle day better?

_____
_____
_____
_____
_____

What is wise to avoid on this cycle day?

What is an activity that syncs up well with this phase of my cycle?

What kind of self-care would make me happier on this cycle day?

_____

_____

_____

_____

_____

_____

What treatments work for health issues I tend to get today?

What can I do today to make tomorrow better?

_____

_____

_____

_____

_____

_____

_____

_____

_____

_____

_____

What can I do today to make the next week of my cycle better?

Accepting that you're affected by the hormones in your cycle does not mean you're acknowledging that you're held back by them.

It means you're wise enough to know that you can harness their benefits and prepare to cope with, or overcome, their challenges to help make every day of your cycle better.

-Gabrielle Lichterman

Cycle Day: _____
Cycle Week: _____

What do I notice about myself on this day in my cycle?

_____
_____
_____
_____
_____
_____

_____
_____
_____
_____
_____

What can I appreciate about this day in my cycle?

How can I make this cycle day better?

_____
_____
_____
_____
_____

What is wise to avoid on this cycle day?

What is an activity that syncs up well with this phase of my cycle?

What kind of self-care would make me happier on this cycle day?

_____

What treatments work for health issues I tend to get today?

_____

What can I do today to make tomorrow better?

_____

What can I do today to make the next week of my cycle better?

_____

Cycle Hack:

Want better sleep all cycle long, and especially on cycle days when solid sleep is more difficult to get? Eat more vegetables! In a study of 3,129 women, those who ate the most vegetables daily fell asleep faster and stayed asleep longer. The researchers credit veggies' rich supply of sleep-promoting nutrients, such as calcium, magnesium, potassium, vitamin C and zinc.

SOURCE:
Ryoko Katagiri, et al., "Low intake of vegetables, high intake of confectionary, and unhealthy eating habits are associated with poor sleep quality among middle-aged female Japanese workers," Journal of Occupational Health, 56 (2014): 359-368

Cycle Day: _____
Cycle Week: _____

What do I notice about myself on this day in my cycle?

_____
_____
_____
_____
_____
_____

_____
_____
_____
_____
_____

What can I appreciate about this day in my cycle?

How can I make this cycle day better?

_____
_____
_____
_____
_____
_____

What is wise
to avoid on
this cycle
day?

_____

_____

_____

_____

_____

What is an
activity that
syncs up
well with
this phase of
my cycle?

_____

_____

_____

_____

_____

What kind of
self-care
would make
me happier
on this
cycle day?

_____

_____

_____

_____

_____

_____

_____

_____

_____

_____

_____

_____

What treatments work for health issues I tend to get today?

What can I do today to make tomorrow better?

_____

_____

_____

_____

_____

_____

_____

_____

_____

_____

_____

What can I do today to make the next week of my cycle better?

Cycle Hack:

Get menstrual migraines (migraines that occur shortly before or during your period) and wonder why sometimes they're worse or more frequent from cycle to cycle? Research shows that menstrual migraine sufferers are more sensitive to other migraine triggers. This means that an odor, food, stress, sleep deprivation, sunlight exposure or another factor that can spur a migraine on its own is more likely to make a head-pounder strike in you, or worsen it, around menstruation.

What can you do about it? Track all your migraine triggers, then try to avoid them, especially as you near menstruation.

SOURCE:
Mei-Ling Sharon Tai, et al., "Geographical Differences in Trigger Factors of Tension-Type Headaches and Migraines," Current Pain and Headache Reports, 21 (2019): 12

Cycle Day: _____
Cycle Week: _____

What do I notice about myself on this day in my cycle?

_____
_____
_____
_____
_____
_____

_____
_____
_____
_____
_____

What can I appreciate about this day in my cycle?

How can I make this cycle day better?

_____
_____
_____
_____
_____
_____

What is wise to avoid on this cycle day?

_____

_____

_____

_____

_____

What is an activity that syncs up well with this phase of my cycle?

_____

_____

_____

_____

_____

What kind of self-care would make me happier on this cycle day?

_____

_____

_____

_____

_____

_____

_____

_____

_____

_____

What
treatments
work for
health issues
I tend to get
today?

What can I
do today to
make
tomorrow
better?

_____

_____

_____

_____

_____

_____

_____

_____

_____

_____

_____

What can I
do today to
make the
next week of
my cycle
better?

This is truly the age of the menstrual cycle.

Never before have we had as much
information about how our cycles work and
impact us daily as we do now.

And collectively we have flipped the
script—turning menstrual cycles from the
butt of jokes to appreciating them as one of
our body's most useful tools for health,
well-being and self-understanding.

-Gabrielle Lichterman

Cycle Day: _____
Cycle Week: _____

What do I notice about myself on this day in my cycle?

_____
_____
_____
_____
_____
_____

_____
_____
_____
_____
_____

What can I appreciate about this day in my cycle?

How can I make this cycle day better?

_____
_____
_____
_____
_____

What is wise to avoid on this cycle day?

What is an activity that syncs up well with this phase of my cycle?

What kind of self-care would make me happier on this cycle day?

What
treatments
work for
health issues
I tend to get
today?

_____
_____
_____
_____
_____
_____

What can I
do today to
make
tomorrow
better?

_____
_____
_____
_____
_____
_____

What can I
do today to
make the
next week of
my cycle
better?

_____
_____
_____
_____
_____

Cycle Hack:

At some points in your cycle, you could have trouble drifting off to sleep or getting back to sleep after waking up because of anxious thoughts. For example, this can occur during your Week 2 (the week leading up to and including ovulation) due to high-and-rising estrogen or during your premenstrual Week 4 due to plunging estrogen.

What can you do to get back to sleep? Recall a funny scene from a movie or TV show. Research shows that thinking of something humorous distracts you from stressors and prompts the flow of feel-good brain chemicals, switching you to a more positive mindset that helps you fall asleep.

SOURCE:
Fatemeh Bahrami, Rahim Kasaei, Ahmadreza Zamani, "Preventing Worry and Rumination by Induced Positive Emotion," International Journal of Preventive Medicine, 3 (2012): 102-109

Cycle Day: _____
Cycle Week: _____

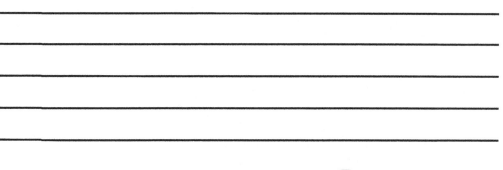

What do I notice about myself on this day in my cycle?

_____
_____
_____
_____
_____
_____

_____
_____
_____
_____
_____

What can I appreciate about this day in my cycle?

How can I make this cycle day better?

_____
_____
_____
_____
_____
_____

What is wise to avoid on this cycle day?

What is an activity that syncs up well with this phase of my cycle?

What kind of self-care would make me happier on this cycle day?

_____
_____
_____
_____
_____
_____

What treatments work for health issues I tend to get today?

What can I do today to make tomorrow better?

_____
_____
_____
_____
_____
_____

_____
_____
_____
_____
_____

What can I do today to make the next week of my cycle better?

Do not be afraid to say that your mood, health or behavior is being influenced by the hormones in your cycle. The era of feeling guilty or ashamed about experiencing hormonal influences is over. It's healthy and empowering to embrace your cycle knowledge and use it for self-understanding.

-Gabrielle Lichterman

Cycle Day: _____
Cycle Week: _____

What do I notice about myself on this day in my cycle?

_____
_____
_____
_____
_____

_____
_____
_____
_____
_____

What can I appreciate about this day in my cycle?

How can I make this cycle day better?

_____
_____
_____
_____
_____

What is wise to avoid on this cycle day?

What is an activity that syncs up well with this phase of my cycle?

What kind of self-care would make me happier on this cycle day?

What treatments work for health issues I tend to get today?

_____

_____

_____

_____

_____

What can I do today to make tomorrow better?

_____

_____

_____

_____

_____

_____

What can I do today to make the next week of my cycle better?

_____

_____

_____

_____

_____

Cycle Hack:

Need a quick boost in mood? Try drinking blueberry juice or purple grape juice. Two small studies show they can rev good feelings in minutes. It's likely because of their high concentration of flavonoids, which increase blood flow to the brain and reduce inflammation—two key factors impacting mood. This is handy information to keep in mind in case low estrogen at the start of your period or descending estrogen in your premenstrual phase has you down. A short glass of blueberry or purple grape juice may boost good feelings again.

Sources:
Crystal Haskell-Ramsay, et al., "Cognitive and mood improvements following acute supplementation with purple grape juice in healthy young adults," European Journal of Nutrition, 56 (2017): 2621-2631
Sundus Khalid, et al., "Effects of Acute Blueberry Flavonoids on Mood in Children and Young Adults," Nutrients, 9 (2017): 158

Cycle Day: _____
Cycle Week: _____

What do I notice about myself on this day in my cycle?

_____
_____
_____
_____
_____

_____
_____
_____
_____
_____

What can I appreciate about this day in my cycle?

How can I make this cycle day better?

_____
_____
_____
_____
_____

What is wise to avoid on this cycle day?

What is an activity that syncs up well with this phase of my cycle?

What kind of self-care would make me happier on this cycle day?

What treatments work for health issues I tend to get today?

_____
_____
_____
_____
_____
_____

What can I do today to make tomorrow better?

_____
_____
_____
_____
_____
_____

What can I do today to make the next week of my cycle better?

_____
_____
_____
_____
_____
_____

Every time I hear someone make a joke about how hormones in a woman's cycle make her cranky, I think... "The joke is on them! Because my hormones also make me brave, confident, happy, adventurous, energetic and funny!"

-Gabrielle Lichterman

Cycle Day: _____
Cycle Week: _____

What do I notice about myself on this day in my cycle?

_____
_____
_____
_____
_____

_____
_____
_____
_____
_____

What can I appreciate about this day in my cycle?

How can I make this cycle day better?

_____
_____
_____
_____
_____

What is wise to avoid on this cycle day?

What is an activity that syncs up well with this phase of my cycle?

What kind of self-care would make me happier on this cycle day?

What
treatments
work for
health issues
I tend to get
today?

_____
_____
_____
_____
_____
_____

What can I
do today to
make
tomorrow
better?

_____
_____
_____
_____
_____
_____

What can I
do today to
make the
next week of
my cycle
better?

_____
_____
_____
_____
_____
_____

You don't have to love your menstrual cycle to be able to use it as a practical tool. It's OK to dislike, even loathe, parts of it.

You'll still be able to use it to predict your mood, health and behavior—which then helps you plan your days ahead.

And, hey, maybe once you see what a useful tool your cycle is, you may like it a smidge more.

-*Gabrielle Lichterman*

Cycle Day: _____
Cycle Week: _____

What do I notice about myself on this day in my cycle?

_____
_____
_____
_____
_____

_____
_____
_____
_____
_____

What can I appreciate about this day in my cycle?

How can I make this cycle day better?

_____
_____
_____
_____
_____

What is wise to avoid on this cycle day?

What is an activity that syncs up well with this phase of my cycle?

What kind of self-care would make me happier on this cycle day?

What treatments work for health issues I tend to get today?

_____
_____
_____
_____
_____

What can I do today to make tomorrow better?

_____
_____
_____
_____
_____
_____

What can I do today to make the next week of my cycle better?

_____
_____
_____
_____
_____
_____

Cycle Hack:

During your Week 3 and Week 4
(the second half of your cycle),
confidence about your body can dip.
This is due to two plunges in estrogen
(which can make you view yourself
more negatively) as well as elevated
progesterone (which can cause bloating).

One easy way to love your body more
in this cycle phase: Pay attention to your
internal signals, such as your heartbeat
and breath. Research shows that being
aware of the wondrous ways your body
works spurs greater appreciation for it
and reduces emphasis on size, shape or
appearance.

SOURCE:
Jennifer Todd, et al., "Multiple dimensions of interoceptive awareness are associated with facets of body image in British adults," Body Image, 29 (2019): 6-16

Cycle Day: _____
Cycle Week: _____

What do I notice about myself on this day in my cycle?

_____
_____
_____
_____
_____

_____
_____
_____
_____
_____

What can I appreciate about this day in my cycle?

How can I make this cycle day better?

_____
_____
_____
_____
_____

What is wise to avoid on this cycle day?

What is an activity that syncs up well with this phase of my cycle?

What kind of self-care would make me happier on this cycle day?

What treatments work for health issues I tend to get today?

_____
_____
_____
_____
_____

What can I do today to make tomorrow better?

_____
_____
_____
_____
_____
_____

What can I do today to make the next week of my cycle better?

_____
_____
_____
_____
_____

"

Compassion
Self-Esteem
Confidence
Understanding
Patience
Acceptance
Love

These are all the things you give
yourself when you know how the
ups and downs of hormones
in your monthly cycle impact
your moods, health and behavior.

-Gabrielle Lichterman

Cycle Day: _____
Cycle Week: _____

What do I notice about myself on this day in my cycle?

_____
_____
_____
_____
_____

_____
_____
_____
_____
_____

What can I appreciate about this day in my cycle?

How can I make this cycle day better?

_____
_____
_____
_____
_____
_____

What is wise to avoid on this cycle day?

What is an activity that syncs up well with this phase of my cycle?

What kind of self-care would make me happier on this cycle day?

What treatments work for health issues I tend to get today?

_____
_____
_____
_____
_____
_____

What can I do today to make tomorrow better?

_____
_____
_____
_____
_____
_____

What can I do today to make the next week of my cycle better?

_____
_____
_____
_____
_____
_____

Learning how the
hormones in your
menstrual cycle impact
your moods, health and
behavior isn't just great
for you and your life.
Once you know, you can
help others understand
themselves and make
their lives better, too.

This knowledge gives
you something
important and
impactful to share that
will make a dramatic
and lasting difference.

-Gabrielle Lichterman

About the Author

Gabrielle Lichterman pioneered the cycle-syncing and hormone awareness movement in 2005 with the first edition of her groundbreaking book, *28 Days: What Your Cycle Reveals About Your Moods, Health and Potential*.

She's the founder of **Hormonology**®—an educational outreach mission that teaches women and girls how hormones impact their moods, health and behavior every day of their cycle. She's also the creator of the popular suite of **Hormone Horoscope** apps for women and teen girls and the **Female Forecaster** app for male partners of cycling women.

Gabrielle is recognized as a leading expert in how cycling hormones impact the brain and body and is a widely-respected women's health journalist who has been at the forefront of covering women's issues for more than 20 years. Her articles have appeared in dozens of major publications around the globe, including *CosmoGirl*, *First for Women*, *Glamour*, *Marie Claire*, *New York Daily News*, *Self*, *Woman's World* and *Working Mother*.

Learn more about Gabrielle and her Hormonology mission at MyHormonology.com.

/hormonology

@hormonology

@hormonology

/hormonology

Made in the USA
Monee, IL
28 June 2021